The Three-Da

Orthodox Christian Easter Stories for Children

Great and Holy Friday

Great and Holy Saturday

Holy Pascha, the Feast of Feasts

Poetry by Mother Melania
with illustrations by Bonnie Gillis

Holy Assumption Monastery
Calistoga, CA
2020

The Three-Day Pascha: Orthodox Christian Easter Stories for Children
Great and Holy Friday
Great and Holy Saturday
Pascha, the Feast of Feasts

ISBN-13: 978-1946991058

Text © copyright 2006 by Mother Melania
Illustrations © copyright 2006 by Bonnie Gillis

Published by Holy Assumption Monastery
1519 Washington St.
Calistoga, CA 94515

Phone: (707) 942-6244
Website: http://holyassumptionmonastery.com
Email: sisters@holyassumptionmonastery.com

For a whimsical look at how to prepare and how NOT to prepare for Pascha, check out

Pascha at the Duck Pond

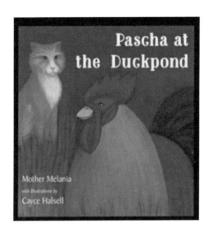

and check out the individual books of the 3-Day Pascha series!

Great and Holy Friday (available soon)

Great and Holy Saturday (available soon)

Pascha, the Feast of Feasts (available soon)

Great and
Holy Friday

The Noble Joseph,

when he had taken down Thy most-pure Body from the tree,

wrapped it in fine linen, anointed it with spices,

and placed it in a new tomb.

Today He who hung the
earth upon the waters is
hung on the Tree,
The King of the angels is decked
with a crown of thorns.
He who wraps the heavens in
clouds is wrapped in the purple
of mockery.
He who freed Adam in the Jor-
dan is slapped on the face.
The Bridegroom of the Church is
affixed to the Cross with nails.
The Son of the Virgin is pierced
by a spear.
We worship Thy passion, O Christ.
We worship Thy passion, O Christ.
We worship Thy passion, O Christ.
Show us also
Thy glorious resurrection.

Antiphon XV
Matins of Great & Holy Friday

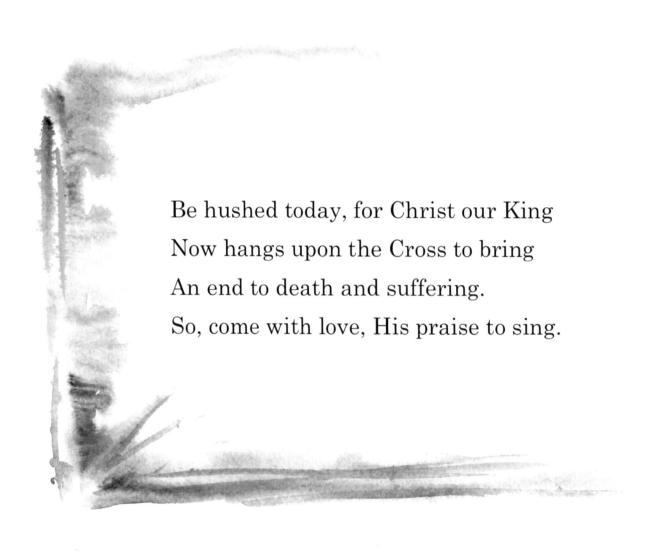

Be hushed today, for Christ our King
Now hangs upon the Cross to bring
An end to death and suffering.
So, come with love, His praise to sing.

Just yesterday,
Cruel judges dared
Condemn Christ God
Who came to bear

The Cross for love
of us, and so
To Golgotha the Savior goes.

The soldiers nail the hands and feet
Of Mary's Holy Son most sweet.
The people mock and offer gall
To Christ, the humble King of all.

The sun goes dark. The mountains shake.
The tombs are split as Jesus takes
Upon Himself all mankind's curse –
The fall of Adam to reverse.

The dying thief repents and cries,
"Remember me!" and Christ replies,
"I tell you truly – you shall be
In paradise today with Me!"

The chief apostle, once so bold,
Denied the Lord, as He foretold,

But faithful John remains beside
The Mother of the Crucified.

The Theotokos weeps to see

Her sinless Son upon the Tree

And cries, 'How can I watch Thee die,

My dearest Child, O God Most High!'

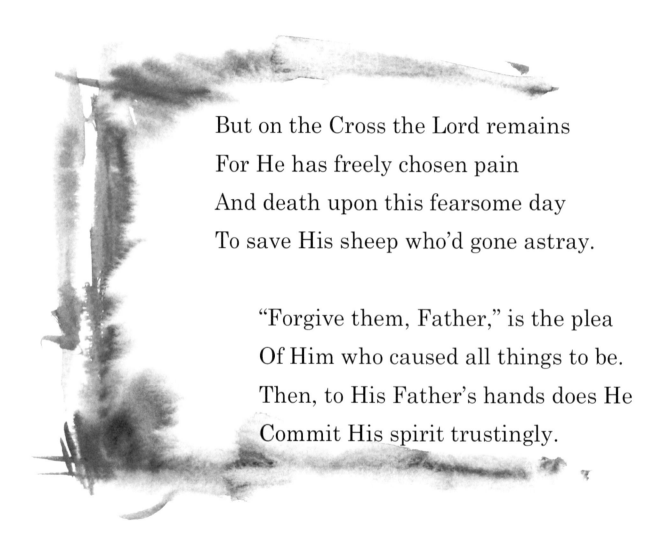

But on the Cross the Lord remains
For He has freely chosen pain
And death upon this fearsome day
To save His sheep who'd gone astray.

"Forgive them, Father," is the plea
Of Him who caused all things to be.
Then, to His Father's hands does He
Commit His spirit trustingly.

He bows His head, the God of Might,
And then He dies – for He is Light
And Life, and cannot die until
He chooses death of His own will.

The soldiers pierce His holy side,
And blood and water flow – a tide
That cleanses us of all our sin
And brings the Life of God within.

For love of Jesus, Who remakes

The world, the Noble Joseph takes

Christ's sinless body and he lays
It in his own new tomb today.

Be hushed, then, for the Deathless One

By dying freely has begun

To flood creation with His joy –

For by His death is death destroyed!

Great and Holy Saturday

Do not lament Me, O Mother, seeing Me in the tomb,
the Son conceived in the womb without seed,
for I shall arise and be glorified with eternal glory as God.
I shall exalt all who magnify thee in faith and in love.

When Thou didst descend to death, O Life Immortal,

Thou didst slay Hades with the splendor of Thy Godhead;

And when from the depths Thou didst raise the dead,

All the powers of Heaven cried out,

"O Giver of Life, Christ our God, glory to Thee!"

– *Resurrectional Troparion (Tone 2)*

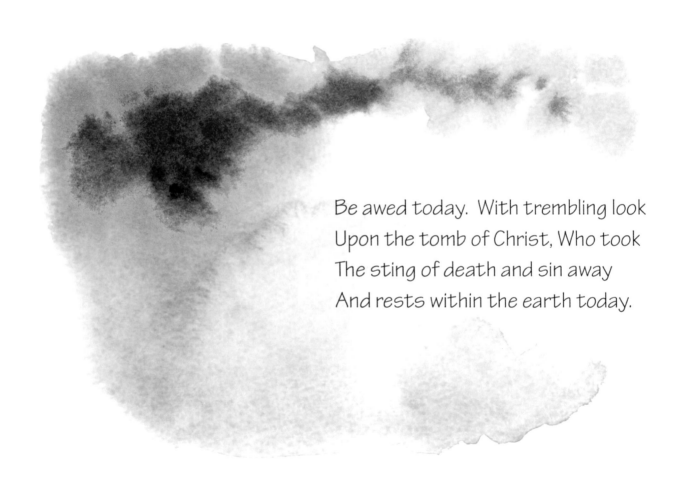

Be awed today. With trembling look
Upon the tomb of Christ, Who took
The sting of death and sin away
And rests within the earth today.

The whole creation wept to see
His death upon the dreadful Tree.
The sun in terror hid his face
When Christ God died for Adam's race!

The Theotokos cries, "My Son!
What have the wicked people done?
How could they dare to murder Thee –
Thou God of Love and Majesty?

"And now what joy is left for me,
Who have no life apart from Thee?
Since Thou, my Child, hast gone away,
O take me with Thee, Lord, I pray!"

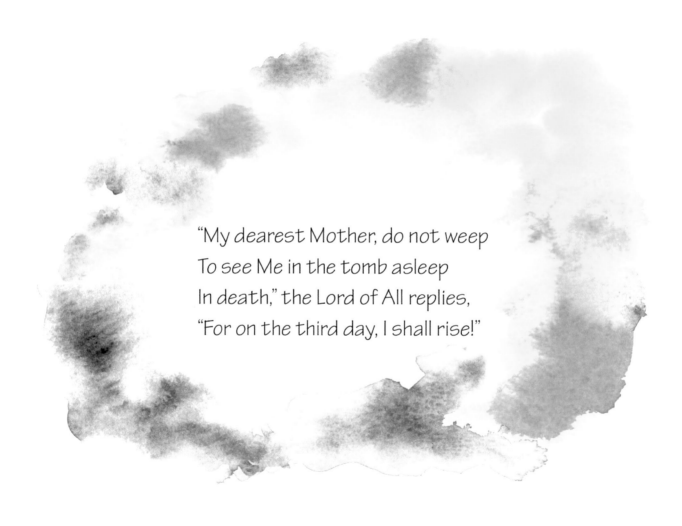

"My dearest Mother, do not weep
To see Me in the tomb asleep
In death," the Lord of All replies,
"For on the third day, I shall rise!"

Note: This icon represents Christ in the tomb. The spear that pierced Christ's side is on Christ's right, the stick on which He was offered vinegar and gall is on His left.

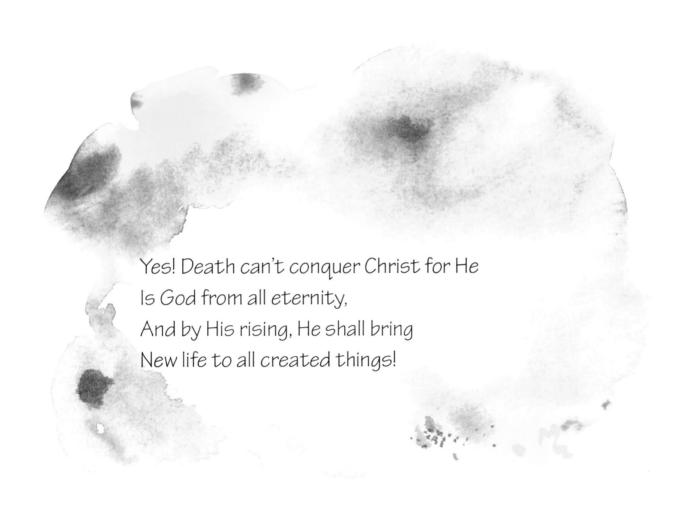

Yes! Death can't conquer Christ for He
Is God from all eternity,
And by His rising, He shall bring
New life to all created things!

And though He has most truly died,
He has not left His Father's side.
For in the heavens, He still reigns
Though in the grave He now remains.

And while He rests within the grave,
Our God, Who came to earth to save,
Releases Hades' captive, who
Through Him are granted life anew.

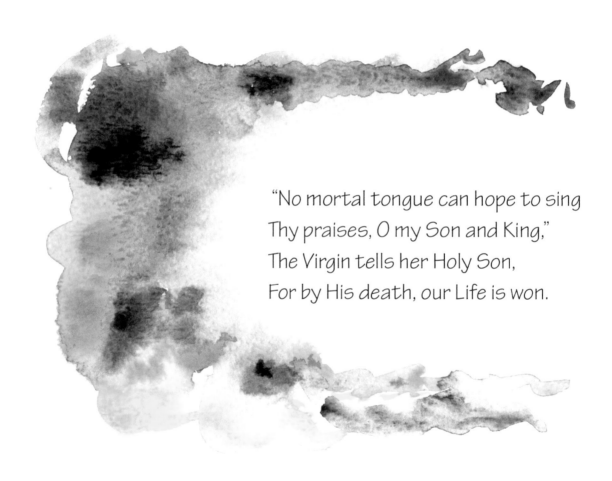

"No mortal tongue can hope to sing
Thy praises, O my Son and King,"
The Virgin tells her Holy Son,
For by His death, our Life is won.

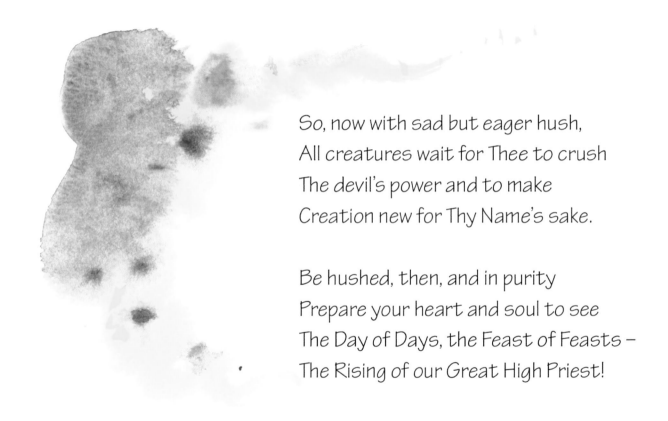

So, now with sad but eager hush,
All creatures wait for Thee to crush
The devil's power and to make
Creation new for Thy Name's sake.

Be hushed, then, and in purity
Prepare your heart and soul to see
The Day of Days, the Feast of Feasts –
The Rising of our Great High Priest!

Note: It is a custom in the Byzantine tradition for the priest to scatter bay leaves around the church during the Liturgy on Holy Saturday afternoon. The leaves represent Christ's victory over death.

Pascha,

The Feast

of Feasts

The angel cried to the Lady Full of Grace:
Rejoice, O Pure Virgin!
Again I say: Rejoice! Thy Son is risen from
His three days in the tomb!
With Himself He has raised all the dead!
Rejoice, all you people!
Shine! Shine! O New Jerusalem!
The Glory of the Lord has shone on thee!
Exalt now and be glad, O Zion!
Be radiant, O Pure Theotokos,
in the Resurrection of thy Son!

Pascha, the Feast of Feasts

(Pascha is known in the West as "Easter")

Christ is risen from the dead,

trampling down death by death,

and upon those in the tombs bestowing life!

– Paschal Troparion

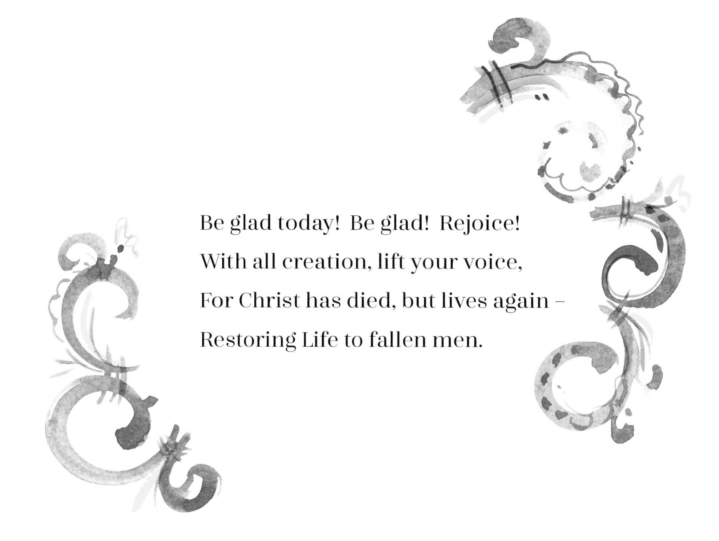

Be glad today! Be glad! Rejoice!

With all creation, lift your voice,

For Christ has died, but lives again –

Restoring Life to fallen men.

Pure Virgin Mother, weep no more.

Thy Son has shattered Hades' doors

For He has gained the victory

O'er death and sets its captives free.

O Mary Magdalene, rejoice

To see Christ's face and hear His voice!

Then, to the Lord's apostles bring

The news of Christ our Risen King!

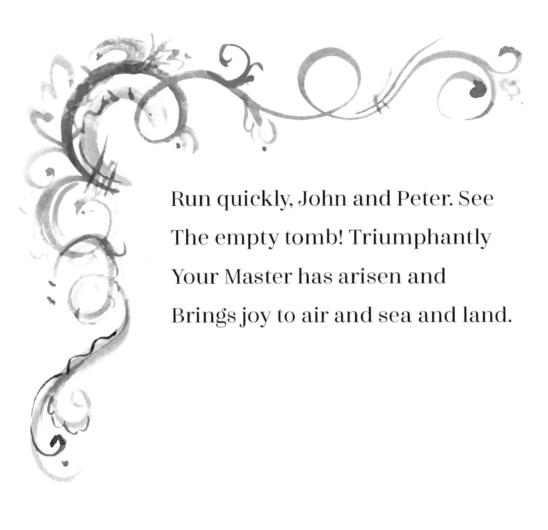

Run quickly, John and Peter. See

The empty tomb! Triumphantly

Your Master has arisen and

Brings joy to air and sea and land.

O myrrhbearers, be glad, I say!

Yes, look! The stone is rolled away!

The grave and death can't hold God's Son –

The King of Kings, the Holy One!

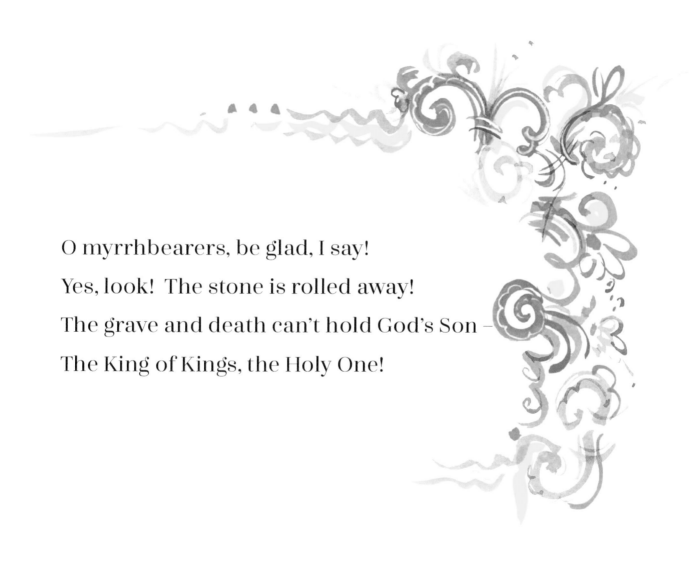

Ye dead, rise up now from the tomb

For Christ has scattered death's dark gloom.

With His divine, eternal Light,

He drives away sin's fearsome night.

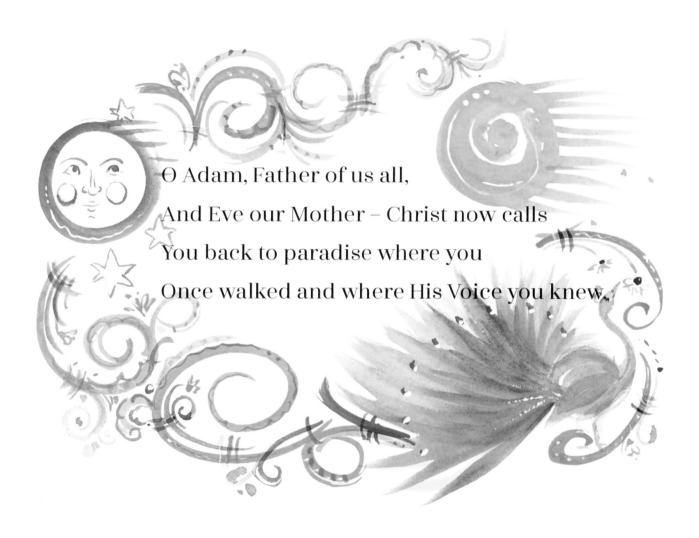

O Adam, Father of us all,

And Eve our Mother – Christ now calls

You back to paradise where you

Once walked and where His Voice you knew.

For He is risen from the dead,

And crushing the foul serpent's head,

He brings to you and all our race

The very fullness of His grace.

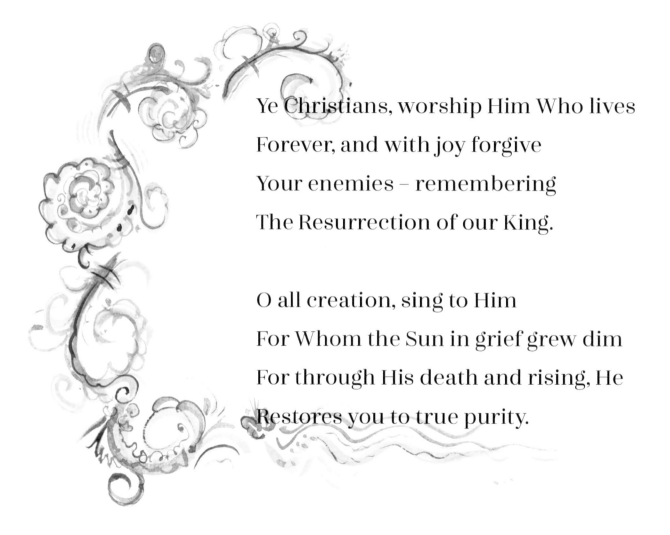

Ye Christians, worship Him Who lives
Forever, and with joy forgive
Your enemies – remembering
The Resurrection of our King.

O all creation, sing to Him
For Whom the Sun in grief grew dim
For through His death and rising, He
Restores you to true purity.

Be glad, be glad! Lift up your hearts!

For Christ is risen and imparts

God's Life to man, and through man pours

That Life on all things – evermore!

Christ is risen!   Truly, He is risen!

Please check out
Mother Melania's other series.

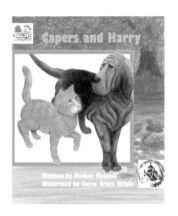

Capers and Harry

from

the Fearless & Friends series

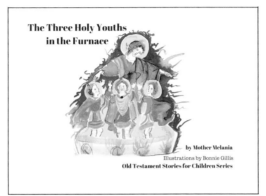

The Three Holy Youths in the Furnace

from

Old Testament Stories for Children

Scooter Gets the Point

from

The Adventures of Kenny & Scooter

Would you please leave a review on this book's Amazon page?

Your feedback helps us to improve!

Thanks so much, and God bless you!

For free work sheets and activity ideas for this book, please email us at

sisters@holyassumptionmonastery.com

Worksheets for

Poetry by Mother Melania

Illustrations by Bonnie Gillis

The
Three-Day
Pascha

Orthodox Christian Easter stories for children

The Three-Day Pascha:
Orthodox Christian Easter
Books for Children -

Volumes 1-3

About THE THREE-DAY PASCHA: Orthodox Christian Easter Stories for Children

Journey with your children through the Three-Day Pascha - the great high point of the story of God's saving love for fallen man and creation. Pascha (the traditional Orthodox name for Easter) is the "Passover" (Pesach) of Christ - and of us through Him - from death to life. So, Great and Holy Friday, Great and Holy Saturday, and the Day of Resurrection are a seamless whole. To think of one without the other two is to misunderstand it.

GREAT AND HOLY FRIDAY (Good Friday) is the ultimate expression of the unspeakable love and humility of God. In the depths of seeming defeat, God's glory - His humble, self-sacrificing love - is clearly seen. So, Orthodox Good Friday services are deeply solemn, yet never gloomy - beneath all the sorrow is a current of joy. Pascha is coming!

GREAT AND HOLY SATURDAY is the Sabbath - the Day of Rest to which all other Sabbaths point. On the seventh day, Christ God rested from the work of creation. Now, after re-creating Man and creation on the Cross, He rests in the tomb on the Great Sabbath. Already, Hades trembles with fear at His presence. Pascha is almost here!

PASCHA is the Day of Resurrection, the day of sheer joy, and the core of the Christian life. Because Christ is risen, we can be healed of our diseases of body and soul and share in God's life because Christ has shared fully in OUR life.

A final note - This series often refers to the Virgin Mary as the Theotokos, which means "the birthgiver of God." This title has been used since at least the third century in order to guard the truth that Mary's Son is not only fully human, but fully God.

ABOUT THE AUTHOR AND ILLUSTRATOR

Mother Melania is the abbess of Holy Assumption Monastery in Calistoga, California. She has enjoyed working with children all of her life. In addition to The Three-Day Pascha series, she has written several other series of children's books, focusing on Scriptural stories and Great Feasts of the Church Feasts, and celebrating virtue.

Bonnie Gillis is an iconographer and illustrator. She lives in Langley, British Columbia, Canada, where her husband, Father Michael, is pastor of Holy Nativity Orthodox Church.

Made in the USA
Columbia, SC
21 January 2024

30342221R00046